This book is dedicated to my family, friends and all the people I have met through tennis. Your belief in me has carried me beyond my wildest imaginations. I challenge you to overcome the obstacles blocking your way... we all can achieve our dreams!

Love for tennis,
Desmond

Library and Archives Canada Cataloguing in Publication

McLennon, Desmond, 1973-
Strings & grips / author: Desmond McLennon;
illustrator: Andre Short.

ISBN 978-0-9812114-1-1

1. Tennis--Juvenile literature. I. Short, Andre, 1980- II. Title.
III. Title: Strings and grips.

GV996.5.M33 2011 j796.342 C2011-900410-0

Cover & Interior Design by Justine Elliott
Editing by Edward Journey

Excelovate

P.O. Box 34021
RPO Hollandview #7
Aurora, Ontario
L4G 0G3

Printed at Webcom

the **Racs**

the **Grips**

Continental   **SEMI WESTERN**   Eastern Backhand   EASTERN

the **Strings**

the **Ball**

Synthetic   Polyester   **KEVLAR**   *Natural*   Nylon

Meet the Team!

We are the Strings strutting down
the street.

And we are the Grips having fun when we meet.

**Follow our program – this is a must
'Cuz we only deal with those we trust.**

There is no discussion, no debate –

Challenge us, you'll know your fate!

**Now is when things begin to change
As our friend Rac comes into the range.**

Rac and his crew make friends with the ball

**To play games
every summer,**

spring,

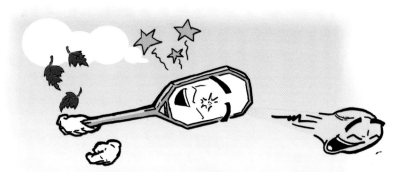

and fall.

To engage the ball and become an ace

Rac wants the Strings to shield his face.

So that he doesn't appear to be gawdy

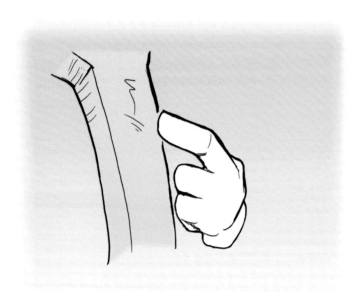

He asks the Grips to guard his body.

The Strings and the Grips agree to help Rac
But he better not cross them or
they may attack.

The Strings help the ball bounce on his face

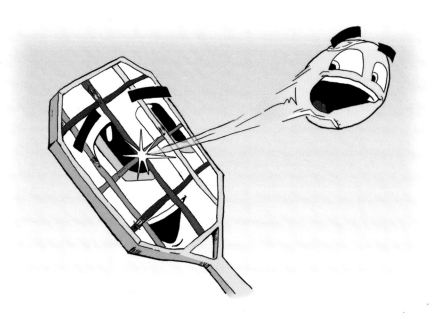

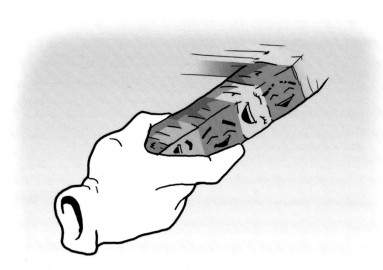

And the Grips hold Rac's body firmly in place.

**They're having such fun hitting the ball
That Rac's whole crew wants to join them all.**

They stake out a place to play around

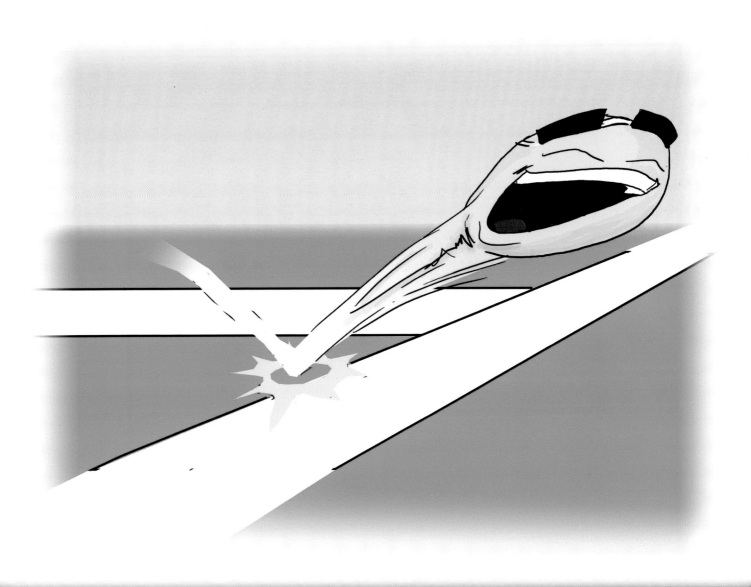

And decide the ball can hit the ground.

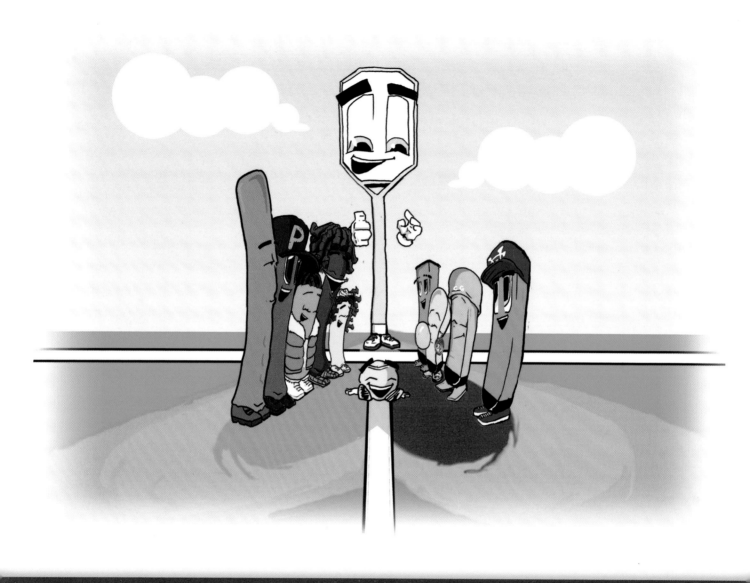

**The Strings and the Grips have
so much pleasure
That they come together to form this treasure.**

They merge their talents to create a fun sport

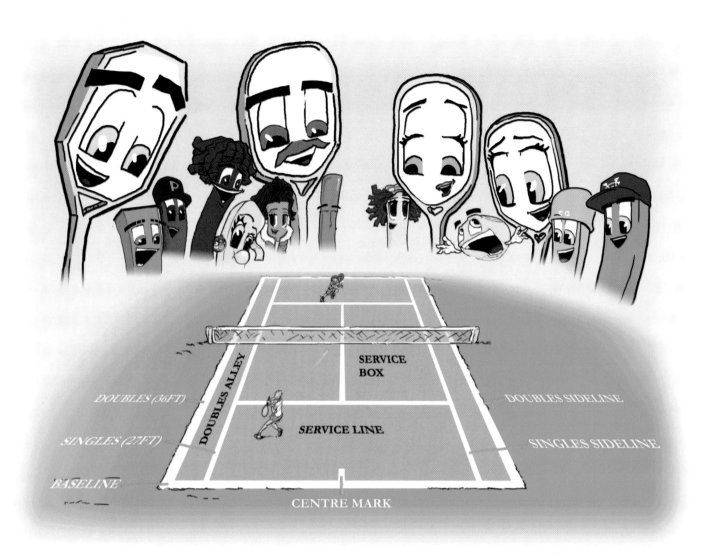

Labels on court diagram:
- SERVICE BOX
- DOUBLES ALLEY
- DOUBLES (36FT)
- SINGLES (27FT)
- BASELINE
- SERVICE LINE
- DOUBLES SIDELINE
- SINGLES SIDELINE
- CENTRE MARK

And call this new home a tennis court.

U.S OPEN

WIMBLEDON

AUSTRALIAN
OPEN

FRENCH OPEN

Nations of the world catch the tennis buzz

And the bouncy little ball takes on some fuzz.

They play on carpet in Russia, and Spain – on clay.

People who play tennis love to play every day.

The Strings and the Grips are a trim
fitness team

Keeping players healthy to fulfill their dream.

No matter where you come from
or when you begin

Grab your tennis racquet and you're sure to win!

Tennis Basics

Every point starts with serving the ball. To serve the ball you get to toss the ball in the air and hit it across the court.

Since this is so much fun – everyone wants to do it first. So, the best way to decide who goes first is to toss a coin and yell out "HEADS!" or scream out "TAILS!".

Now for some Scoring Basics:

1. POINTS

Each player starts with 0 points.

1st point = 15
2nd point = 30
3rd point = 40
4th point = game

Everyone WINS!

2. GAMES

The first player to win at least 6 games wins the set.

3. SETS

When you win 2 out of 3 sets, you win the entire match.

4. MATCHES

Whether you win or lose, always end each match with a handshake.

Important Things to Remember

- Zero (0) points is also known as "Love" in Tennis.
- You need to win at least 4 points to win a game.
- It takes a minimum of 6 games to win a set.
- Win 2 out of 3 sets and you win the match.
- When the score is 40-40, this is also called "Deuce."
- The player who gets the first point after "Deuce" is referred to as having the "Advantage."

To win in the game of Tennis, you need to be ahead of your opponent by:

- 2 points to win the game
- 2 games to win the set
- 2 sets to win the match

Always remember...
Game – Set – Match!